THE FIRST POETRY KIT

Moira Andrew   David Orme

Stanley Thornes (Publishers) Ltd

First published in 1990 by:
Stanley Thornes (Publishers) Ltd
Old Station Drive
Leckhampton
CHELTENHAM GL53 0DN
England

British Library Cataloguing in Publication Data
Andrew, Moira
 The first poetry kit.
 1. Great Britain. Primary schools. Curriculum subjects:
 Poetry in English. Teaching
 I. Title   II. Orme, David
 372.64

 ISBN 0–7487–0435–3

Typeset by Goodfellow & Egan, Cambridge
Printed and bound in Great Britain by Ebenezer Baylis & Son Ltd, Worcester

Contents

Acknowledgements

The authors and publishers wish to thank the following who have kindly given permission for the use of copyright material:

John Cotton for 'The first lick of the lolly' on *Best First Things* ● Sue Cowling for 'Asking Questions' on *Asking Questions* ● John Kitching for 'I like Soft-boiled Eggs' on *Good Things to Eat* ● Gerda Mayer for 'Paper Boat' on *Paper Boat* ● Judith Nicholls for 'What can you do with a pencil? on *What can you do with a . . . ?* ● Ernest Rogers for 'Snake' on *Mini-beast Poems* ● Colleen Thibaudeau for 'Balloon' on *Balloons and Kites* ●

Every effort has been made to trace all copyright holders, and we apologise if any have been overlooked.

The drawings in this book are by Andrew Keylock.

The cover photograph has been reproduced by kind permission of ZEFA.

Use of the Poetry Kit sheets

The *First Poetry Kit* sheets have been carefully prepared to provide both structure and progression through the various stages of poetry writing in the primary school. On the earliest sheets a simple single-word response is called for; by the end of the course in the *Second Poetry Kit* the children are asked to work in a quite sophisticated way using image, syllable count and pattern.

Teachers may wish to use the *First Poetry Kit* in a number of different ways:

1 as a class lesson to introduce a new writing skill;
2 for a group of children at the same stage of development;
3 as a profitable 'end-on' activity for children who have completed a class/group task;
4 as a consolidation exercise for a child who is having problems with more difficult work.

Although the sheets are arranged with a clear idea of progression in mind, teachers may wish to select sheets to suit a particular task for individual children.

Many of the sheets have extension ideas. These are intended for children who may want to do further work on their own and provide imaginative activities for the ablest pupils. Sheets are designed to follow this plan:

sheet idea	→	rough work	→	best work	→	extension
(task)		(editing)		(presentation)		(child's own interpretation)

Structuring your Poetry Work

Poetry writing is often thought of as an *ad hoc*, inspirational activity, and no one would wish to deny the importance of what we call the imaginative leap in poetry. The poems we value most highly are the ones that astonish us; unlike other areas of the curriculum, we value the unexpected response. This does not make the assessment process easy. However, like any art form, the ability to surprise comes from a high level of skill. Built into the *First Poetry Kit* materials are word games, exercises in vocabulary-building, poetry patterns and forms, rhyme and rhythm, and performance, which are the strands that run through a structured poetry teaching programme. As is made clear in *English from 5–16*, development of skills is recursive, and these elements repeat themselves at increasingly demanding levels through the materials.

The grid on page 5 shows which of these elements are emphasised in each page, and can be of use in achieving specific attainment targets. All pages feature these elements to some extent, and all will provide practice in reading, writing, talking and listening.

Poetry in the Infant Classroom

The *First Poetry Kit* aims to capitalise on the children's own language experience. Children arrive at school with highly developed linguistic skills, a joy in words and a quite sophisticated appreciation of rhythm. They are ready to talk, to act, to listen and to participate fully in the business of communication. The *First Poetry Kit* builds on this base, providing a range of enjoyable exercises to enlarge vocabulary and extend the imaginative use of words, and children at all levels of attainment are encouraged to take part in making up poems and rhymes.

A First Introduction to Poetry

Poetry should be introduced to the youngest children as an enjoyable listening activity, perhaps as part of story-time, when they are gathered together informally. The lucky ones will be familiar already with traditional nursery rhymes, finger plays and songs but will delight in their repetition. Those who come new to them will soon learn to respond and to join in. Nursery rhymes provide a way in to the skill of listening and act as a sound foundation on which to build the teaching of poetry.

Teachers can encourage 'attentive listening' (Key Stage One, AT1 L1 and 2) by dropping end words of nursery rhymes and asking the children to fill them in. They might then, orally, make up new rhymes which follow the original pattern.

In addition to books of nursery rhymes and finger plays, teachers should try to build up a collection of poetry anthologies. Aim to introduce a couple of new poems every other day. Read them again and again. Repetition is the name of the game.

When a new poem is to be introduced it is a good idea to talk around it first, so that the children have a key to the poem before they hear it. It can be read first without comment, then read again, this time asking questions e.g:

How does the poem make you feel?
Why do you like/dislike this poem?
What might happen next?

Try to use open questions so that the children have a real chance of responding to what they have heard. Allow some discussion among the group: most comments are valid. This activity could be followed up by some drama suggested by the poem, or in making pictures and paintings to illustrate it. (Key Stage One, AT1 L2).

It is important to let the children become familiar with a poem over a period of time. This way it grows into their consciousness and allows them to possess it as their own. (That is what happens with nursery rhymes. We all 'possess' them, even as adults.)

Now, and only now, is the time to dissect the poem. Encourage the children to listen for rhyme and for rhythm (the beat). Talk about whether it is a fast or slow poem, funny, serious or sad, a story poem, a tongue twister, a joke or a describing poem. Let the children see the pattern the words make on the page. Such activities develop active listening skills and encourage thoughtful response. (Key Stage One, AT1 L2, 'listen attentively, and respond, to . . . poems.')

The next step is for the children to take part in making up poems with the help of the teacher. The very youngest can enjoy and learn from this activity. The teacher, who effectively takes the role of secretary, should use a clipboard and felt-tip pen. Ask the children to look closely at some familiar natural object: shell, flower, twig, fruit, stone etc. Encourage them to contribute words to describe the *look* of the object and write these words clearly in list form. Read the words back to the children and ask for comments about how well the words would give a picture if the object were hidden. Repeat for words about touch, then taste, smell and/or hearing if these are appropriate. Assemble the words together in clusters on another sheet of paper. Choose and discard words in discussion with the children. This is a simple form of editing, a skill which the children will use for themselves later.

To describe a grapefruit the group may have come up with:

round, yellow, squashy, juicy
smells lemony, tickles your nose
tastes sour, sharp, like medicine.

A simple poem from this list would go something like this:

The grapefruit is round and yellow.
It feels squashy and juicy, quite heavy.
It smells lemony and tickles your nose.
It tastes sour and sharp, like medicine.
We have grapefruit for breakfast on Sundays.

Let the children watch the process of editing and producing a rough draft; then copy the poem out in 'best'. Read the poem back to the children, then get them to say it aloud. This encourages the link between symbols and meaning (Key Stage One, AT2 L1, recognition that 'print carries meaning').

Using this technique the teacher is demonstrating a simple method of drafting and editing which the children can copy. She will encourage a search for descriptive words and give the children the confidence to build up their own list poems: a successful way of working for even the youngest or least-able pupils (Key Stage One AT3 L2 'simple, coherent non-chronological writing').

A further step in the production of a group poem is to suggest some images e.g:
    round as a ball, round as the sun, round as a witch's face,
    like a yellow balloon, like a juicy lollipop, like a squashy sponge.
The poem might change its style:

A grapefruit is as round as the sun.
It is like a yellow balloon.
It is as squashy as a wet sponge.
It smells lemony and tickles your nose.
It tastes like a juicy lollipop.
It tastes sour and sharp, like medicine.
It looks like a witch's scary face.
It looks like a Hallowe'en lantern.
We have grapefruit for breakfast on Sundays.

The use of image encourages children to 'play' with language and to find out what language can do in a creative sense. When the teacher reads over the group rough draft she should emphasise the rhythm or beat of the words. Children soon come to know when a single-beat or two-beat word is called for. This lays the ground for syllable counting at a later stage.

By example, the teacher can encourage children to work from word lists to rough draft, to best writing or word processor. Word lists set the scene for the writer and help to get the mind in gear for the task ahead. Easy access to the finished group poem is essential so that the children have the opportunity of reading a familiar piece of work and consolidating the link between symbol and meaning. Use a wall display, a large zig-zag book or put together an anthology of group poems for the library shelf. The children can provide suitable illustrations (Key Stage One, AT2 L1 . . . 'begin to recognise words . . . in familiar contexts.')

Preparation

When the children are at the stage of beginning to write for themselves and can put together a simple word list they are ready to tackle the early *First Poetry Kit* sheets. At first it may be advisable for the teacher to introduce each sheet to a small group of children at a similar stage of development.

The teacher should take time to look at the sheet with the children and talk through the instructions. She should help the children to collect and share ideas orally, reassure them that spelling does not matter at this stage and provide them with paper on which to make word lists and try out their rough work. Let the children score out rather than rub out. An outpouring of ideas is important, not necessarily neatness or correctness. As long as the rough work is readable, it is acceptable. Be ready with support, assistance with spelling and plenty of encouragement as the rough work is made ready for transfer to the sheets. When the children are happy with what they have written, let them fill in and colour and/or cut up their own individual sheets. It is important that the children should enjoy the task of writing and have a sense of fulfilment when it is successfully completed.

Using a Sheet: What's in the Box?

This is a good example of a sheet to use with a group of beginners. It can be used as the basis of a group poem with those who are ready to write, later allowing some to progress to work individually on their own sheet.

Show the picture of the 'secret box', or better still, bring in a tiny pill box. Suggest to the children that the box might be magic, that a tiny secret creature lives inside. Make up a word list of small creatures from the children's suggestions, e.g:
    ant
    caterpillar
    spider
    bee

3

Now ask what each creature looks like and extend your list to *red* ant, *striped* caterpillar, *scary* spider etc.

Then take movement suggestions so that you have perhaps:

a red ant *scurrying*

a striped caterpillar *crawling*

a scary spider *spinning* etc.

Use these ideas to make a list poem beginning 'Inside the box lives . . .' If the children are encouraged to listen to the rhythm of the words some most effective work can be built up, first as a group poem, then as individual pieces. The children can decorate the box with felt-tip pen and draw lots of tiny creatures to illustrate their poems.

Assessment

Whether or not poetry work can be assessed is a subject of much disagreement. The authors feel that poetry writing has some assessable elements, and some elements that are rather more elusive. It is difficult to have a yardstick to measure outcomes when, as we have said, the most desirable outcome is often the most unexpected. Other elements can be assessed: developing vocabulary, writing confidence, understanding of complex ideas; but only in terms of individual development of the pupil.

Many teachers are concerned that they have no personal yardstick for measuring the 'quality' of a poem, over and above any personal development that might have taken place. Children have no such problems; either a poem 'works' for them or it does not. They are assessing a poem in terms of impression, and personal impact, and teachers should feel free to assess in the same way. Thus a positive comment on a poem is of value; a mark or grade has no value or meaning at all.

The *First Poetry Kit* and the National Curriculum

The *First Poetry Kit* has been designed to enable children to work towards the attainment targets demanded by the National Curriculum.

As children work through the sheets an increasing emphasis is placed on the importance of word lists and rough drafts. These activities gradually build up the children's skill in drafting and editing before the final presentation of their writing. (Key Stage One, AT3 L3 'Pupils should be able to begin to revise and redraft . . .').

Many of the *First Poetry Kit* sheets suggest that children take into consideration the shape and pattern that words make on paper. Such a discipline helps them to look for the 'best words in the best order' and to eliminate anything that is fussy or over-elaborate (Key Stage One, AT3 2 'simple, coherent non-chronological writing').

From the earliest pages of the *First Poetry Kit* to those at the end of the *Second Poetry Kit* children are encouraged to use the idea of image. This leads them ultimately towards simile and metaphor. It helps them to produce vivid descriptive language 'with detail beyond simple events . . .' (Key Stage One, AT3 L3).

Pupils are introduced to use punctuation: capital letters, question marks and speech marks and are encouraged to use 'a range of sentence connectives' (Key Stage One, AT3 3).

Many of the *First Poetry Kit* starters are designed to enable children to 'produce, independently, pieces of writing [some] using complete sentences', (Key Stage One, AT3 L3), but all will build confidence in the task of writing. The children are encouraged to use a range of ways in which to set out their work: shape poems, chorus poems, mini-poems, postcard poems, alphabet poems. They can write and draw directly on the sheets, colour and cut them up. When some of the poems are finished the children can even sail them, fly them or wear them as masks! One of our main aims in the preparation of the book, therefore, is that children should find poetry writing an enjoyable, successful and rewarding activity.

Key Elements in the Pupils' Sheets

	Words	Patterns	Sounds	Images	Making/Display
Colour the Sun				1	1
Animal Pictures				1	
New Nursery Rhymes			1		
Balloons and Kites	1				
Spider Plant				2	
Jigsaw		2			1
The Magic Box	2				2
Five Fat Frogs		2			
Monsters	2				
What's in the Pudding?	2	2			
Poetry Clock		2			2
What's in the Box?	2	2			
Weather Words	2		2		
Flying Poems		2		2	
Summer is . . .				2	
The Quietest Thing in the World	2	2			
Best First Things	2		2		
Chorus Poems		2	2		2
Days of the Week				2	
Sad Face, Happy Face	2			2	2
Magic Spell	2			2	
Expanding Poems		3		3	
Good Things to Eat	3			3	
Wind Streamers				3	2
Angry Child, Happy Child	3			3	
Christmas Chains				3	2
Paper Boat					3
Holiday Postcards		3			3
Noisy Traffic		3	3		
What can you do with a . . . ?	3	3			
Animal Parade	3		3		
Puppet Talk					3
Coloured Flags				3	3
Our Garden Shed	3				
Mini-beast Poems		3			
House Poem	3			3	
The Magic Key				3	3
The Fantastic Forest	3			3	
Asking Questions		3		3	

The numbers indicate
level of difficulty

Teacher's Notes

Notes on the Use of Each Sheet

Colour the Sun
Materials Rough paper, pencils, ruler, coloured pencils or felt tips.
Discussion Talk about warmth, colour, light etc. How does it feel on a sunny day?
Use Make a word list. Write ideas on the rays of the sun.
Extension Make a moon, star or cloud poem using the same idea. Think of a hedgehog or a porcupine with ideas written along the spikes.

Animal Pictures
Materials Pencils, coloured pencils or felt tips.
Discussion Talk about pets the children have, would like to have. Talk about size, shape, movement, noises.
Extension Make a gallery of pictures and words about pets. Put the poems and pictures in a frame. Make a pictogram/graph of favourite pets.

New Nursery Rhymes
Materials A selection of nursery rhyme books for the children to look at. Rough paper, pencils, coloured pencils or felt tips.
Discussion Read and listen to a selection of nursery rhymes. Talk about end rhymes. Listen to 'Mary had a little lamb'. Think of a different pet; cat, dog, fish etc.
Use Make up new rhymes about Terry and his mouse, Sally and her hen. Follow the 'Mary had a little lamb' model.
Extension Make up new nursery rhymes and paste up into a classroom book.

Balloons and Kites
Materials Rough paper, pencils, felt tips, scissors, string or wool.
Discussion Talk about balloons, kites, paper aeroplanes, autumn leaves; things that fly in the wind. List images to follow 'as big as ball', e.g. 'as high as clouds', 'as light as feathers'.
Use Fill in the kite shape. Colour and cut out. Follow words with a 'tail' of glued-on string or wool. Make a class frieze.
Extension Use the same idea for hot air balloons.

Spider Plant
Materials Spider plant, pencils, scissors, glue or paste, felt tips.
Discussion Look closely at a spider plant. Look at the way in which the leaves 'flow' from the centre. Talk about what they look like, i.e. discuss images. Like 'a wave crashing over rocks', 'a scarf round a snowman's neck' etc. Encourage unusual ideas.
Use Write ideas on the leaf shape. Colour carefully and cut out. Make a class picture with the leaves pasted flat. (Some of the work should be done on the back of the shape so that both sides of the picture are complete.) You could make a spider plant mobile that hangs from the ceiling.

Jigsaw
Materials Scissors, card, pencils, paste.
Use Paste the sheet on to thin card. Allow to dry. Cut out and mix. Assemble as a jigsaw.
Extension Photocopy the jigsaw template and use with other poems, either those made up by the children or copied as 'favourites' from a class anthology. Let the children work in pairs, each assembling the other's poem.

The Magic Box
Materials Rough paper, pencils, coloured pencils or felt tips.
Discussion Talk about buried treasure, what people might find in a box lost for many years. Introduce the idea that the box might be magic. Read Chloe's poem. Gather more magic ideas from the children. Write out the ideas in rough and help them select the most exciting.
Use Write individual or group ideas into the box. Colour and put small neat illustrations around the list.
Extension Make a class display or class poem in an outlined box, lid open to reveal the poems. Mix the poems with real 'treasures' e.g. old beads or coins in an open box as an entrance hall display.

Five Fat Frogs
Materials Pencils, felt tips, scissors, thin card.
Discussion Read and talk about counting rhymes. Introduce 'Five fat frogs' and ask for suggestions to finish each verse. Look for rhyming words.
Extension Make up a new counting poem using cats, tin cans, butterflies, witches, grannies . . .

Monsters
Materials Rough paper, pencils, felt tips, paints, rulers, card.
Discussion Talk about Trog, the Monster. Friendly or unfriendly? Where are

6

the clues? Show the way the poem is written. Point out speech marks. Ask children to think of a monster and how it might look.

Use Collect ideas about how each monster looks, what he is made of etc. Write out a list in rough. Choose the most exciting ideas and let each child make his own poem. Encourage awareness of speech marks. Illustrate.

Extension Make a monster frieze with painted or cut-out monster shapes. Leave room for speech bubbles (as in comics) and write individual poems in the speech bubbles. Make up a monster drama/play. Make masks taped to rulers so that they can hold them away from their faces as they read.

What's in the Pudding?

Materials Recipe books with pictures, rough paper, pencils, felt tips.

Discussion Look at the way recipes are laid out. Look at the pictures and talk about the ingredients. Read the poem 'What's in the pudding?' Talk about what odd things go into it. Ask for suggestions. Encourage the fantastic. Show the children the pattern that makes up the poem.

Use Make out a list of fantastic ingredients for 'What's in the stew?' (The poem doesn't have to rhyme, but watch the rhythm.) Write into the space and illustrate.

Extension Make up a class recipe book for fantastic salads, soup, pies, etc.

Poetry Clock

Materials Rough paper, pencils, scissors, pencil crayons or felt tips.

Discussion Talk about times of the day and what happens at particular times e.g. 'home time', TV time, tea-time, bath time etc. Read the poem and collect ideas for a new clock poem. Point out that the poet has made mini-poems to describe what happens at the end of school and after.

Use Use rough paper to collect ideas for individual mini-poems. Encourage the children to make them short and to watch line length. When they are happy with their mini-poems, write them carefully in the space provided. Then cut out and colour the clock and slot the poem through the spaces. The heavy black lines are cutting lines.

Extension Make up mini-mini poems (one word on a line).

What's in the Box?

Materials Small pill box, rough paper, pencils, coloured pencils or felt tips.

Discussion Suggest that a tiny magic creature might live in the box. Ask children to guess what it could be. Write some of the guesses in a list on the board or on a large sheet of paper. (Write the list down the middle of the sheet.) Ask for colour ideas so that you may have a *silver* spider, a *rainbow* worm, (writing descriptive words on the left of the sheet). Then talk about how the creatures move; 'a silver spider *spinning*,' 'a rainbow worm *wriggling*' etc.

Use Get the children to write down a list of their guesses on rough paper. When they are happy with the list, and it sounds right (i.e. they have done a rhythm check), write it into the space. It will make a poem. Colour the box and draw the tiny magic creatures around the sides.

Weather Words

Materials Rough paper, pencils, felt tips or coloured pencils.

Discussion Every day has its weather and every kind of weather has its own words to describe it. Take the children outside on a wet day or look and listen from the classroom. Make a list of rainy day words.

Use Invite the children to write their words on rough paper until the words make a song inside their heads, i.e. check the rhythm. Arrange the words across the umbrella shape in lines of rain. Use fine felt tip pens.

Extension Use the same idea for thunder and lightning. Think of the crashing noise of thunder, the jagged shape lightning makes.

Flying Poems

Materials Pencils, scissors, rough paper.

Discussion Talk about how wonderful it would be to be able to fly. What must it feel like? Look at pictures of birds and butterflies and other flying creatures. Help the children to look for images of flying e.g. like hot-air balloons soaring over the fields, like autumn leaves in the wind.

Use Fill in the spaces on the sheet with flying images. Then write them in poem form on the glider shape. Cut it out, fold and let it fly across the classroom as a flying poem.

Extension Make sailing poems, floating poems and pull-along poems.

Summer is . . .

Materials Rough paper, pencils, wax crayons or felt tips.

Discussion Talk about the hot days of summer. Think about what makes summer so special. Encourage the children to think of their own 'summer specials' and to make a picture of summer in their imaginations.

Use Write the ideas on rough paper. Start each idea with the words 'Summer is . . .' Select the most unusual and write them on a sunflower petal. Carefully outline each petal in yellow, or use wax crayon sparingly to colour across the words.

Extension Make a sunflower garden on deep blue backing paper as a classroom or group display. Cut out the sunflower poems and paste them at different heights on the frieze. Make daisy, buttercup or dandelion friezes.

The Quietest Thing in the World

Materials Pencils, rough paper, felt tips or pencil crayons.

Discussion Talk about all the tiniest and/or quietest creatures the children can think of. Think about how they move, what songs they might sing if they could. Try to encourage an imaginative response.

Use Write down ideas on rough paper. Colour the pictures and fill in the other spaces. Select the most imaginative ideas, correct spelling if necessary and ask the children to write their poems into the space.

Extension Use the same idea to make up a poem about the noisiest creatures in the world, the tallest, smallest or wriggliest etc.

Best First Things

Materials Rough paper, pencils, felt tips or pencil crayons.

Discussion Read John Cotton's poem aloud. Talk about best first things. Encourage talk about how exciting some of those first time things were.

Use Write a list on rough paper. Say them over until the rhythm is right and arrange them in poem form inside the number shape. John Cotton's poem rhymes, but this one doesn't have to rhyme.

Chorus Poems

Materials Scissors, pencils, rough paper.

Discussion Read a couple of poems with a chorus. Get the children to join in. Read 'Listen to the band'. Get to know the chorus. Take suggestions for new verses using the names of children in the class. Make it fun.

Use Ask children, individually or in groups, to put down ideas (in a four-line format) on rough paper. Transfer mini-poems to the sheet. Cut out and thread through the TV screen. Individuals can read verses, the rest of the group join in the chorus.

Extension Use the other side of the poetry strip to make another chorus poem, about a visit to the park, playing in the playground, joining a sports team etc. Try to elicit a chorus first, followed by verses.

Days of the Week

Materials Pencils, rough paper, felt tips or coloured pencils.

Discussion Talk about what happens in school on different days of the week. Do they like or not like that particular day? Talk about how the children feel. Ask what their happiest or saddest colour is.

Use The children should first fill in the chart, then use rough paper to outline their poems. Fill in the calendar and colour.

Extension Use a similar idea to make a year calendar, suggesting what special things each month brings. Look for a colour to go with each month.

Sad Face, Happy Face

Materials Pencils, thin card, scissors, felt tips, rough paper.

Discussion Talk about the expressions on faces. What tells us that someone feels happy or sad? Talk in pairs about words to express feelings.

Use Make word collections on the appropriate mask. Cut out masks from thin card. Make one look happy, the other unhappy. Let the pair make up a conversation, (liking/not liking school dinners, liking/not looking forward to PE/maths etc.) Write the conversation out on rough paper. When they are happy with it, transfer the 'poem' to best work using a different coloured pencil for each voice.

Extension Make a conversation poem into a short play and perform it at assembly. Use masks taped to rulers.

Magic Spell

Materials Pencils, rough paper, felt tips or coloured pencils.

Discussion Talk about Hallowe'en and magic spells. Let the children go to town on all the disgusting things which they would like to put in a spell. Ask how the spell is to be used. Look for magic words to make a chorus for the spell. Try 'Abra-cadabra!' or 'Fat Black cats!' or 'Smelly Cabbages!' Read 'Eye of snake'. Look for the rhyming words.

Use Let children make up a last verse for 'Eye of snake'; it should rhyme this time. Then put together another poem on rough paper using some of the nasty ingredients they have thought about. (This is a good place to show how well rhyme works when the poem is intended to be funny.) Transfer the poem to their own witch's cauldron. Decorate.

Expanding Poems

Materials Pencils, rough paper, unlined A4 paper.

Discussion Fold the poetry sheet as shown. Read 'Movements' across i.e. without the images: 'A black cat slinks through the grass. A long snake glides beneath a hot stone' etc. Ask what a cat might look like. Note the ideas. Then expand the poem and read 'Movements' again. Talk about the pattern of the poem. Discuss the images. Is a black cat really like a long snake? Did the children have a better idea? What other images could be used? Show the children how the poems expand. Talk about images to fill in 'Bonfire Night'.

Use Ask the children to find their own images for rockets etc. so that they can fill in the sheet. Watch how the poems can be folded and expanded.

Extension Experiment with more expanding poems. 'A prickly hedgehog is like', 'a slimy slug is like', 'a spotted ladybird is like' etc.

Good Things to Eat

Materials Pencils, rough paper, felt tips or coloured pencils.

Discussion Talk about things children like/don't like, and why. Make a word list.

Use The children make up a list of things they like best to eat. Encourage extension of the ideas, so that the list develops into a poem.

Extension Make menu cards and food poems for a wall display. Make up poems about best-liked pets (some fabulous), best-liked relatives or a school timetable poem written as an extended list.

Wind Streamers

Materials Pencils, rough paper, thin sticks (plant props are ideal), drawing pins or sticky tape, scissors.

Discussion Listen to the sound of the wind. Talk about what kind of wind there is. Is it a gentle breeze? Is it a strong stormy wind? Try to find the sound the wind is making in the trees, leaves, telephone wires, chimney pots. Make a word list of windy day sounds.

Use Collect ideas from the word list. Write individual lines on the paper strips. Cut out and pin or tape to a stick. Run outside and fly the poems.

Angry Child, Happy Child

Materials Pencils, felt tips or coloured pencils.

Discussion Talk about what makes people angry, how they feel. What is an angry kind of colour? Talk about what you feel when you are happy. Make word lists of angry and happy words. What do people say when they are angry or happy?

Use Use speech bubbles to fill in what angry and happy people say. Draw angry and happy faces. Make up a poem in pairs using different feelings, different words. Note how actual words used are put into the speech bubbles.

Extension Make comic-type strips using the speech bubbles. (This is a starter for the use of speech marks.)

Christmas Chains

Materials Pencils, coloured pencils, scissors, glue or paste.

Discussion Talk about Christmas and what it means to different people. Talk about sentences. Suggest that they make up sentences beginning with the words 'Christmas is . . .'

Use Make up the ideas list. Put the ideas into sentences. Write one sentence on each strip. Colour carefully with coloured pencil so that the words are visible. Cut out and paste or glue into chains for decorating the classroom.

Paper Boat

Materials Pencils, felt tips, scissors.

Discussion Read Gerda Mayer's poem 'Paper boat'. Talk about sailing away across the ocean in a boat. What adventures could you have on the way? Have the children suggest storybook names for their boat. Talk about messages in bottles and suggest that the children might like to write a 'bottle' message in the their boat.

Use Let the children write out their message poem in the space on the boat. Let them cut and fold, following the pattern. They might like to try sailing the boat across a puddle, or use the water tank in the classroom.

Holiday Postcards

Materials Pencils, felt-tip pens, scissors.

Discussion Talk about sending postcards home from holiday. Who do we send them to? What kind of things do we say on postcards? We must keep the message quite short. Look at the outlined postcard scenes on the sheets. Ask what children might want to say about them to people at home. Make a list of ideas. Read 'Summer picture'. Look at the way two of the words sit by themselves on a line. This gives the poem a shape (a bit like a butterfly?) and makes the two movement words 'dances' and 'fluttering' look very important.

Use Let the children use rough paper to jot down their own ideas from the pictures. When they are happy with their efforts, let them write their postcard poems on the back of the picture. Colour the outline pictures.

Extension Make a selection of 'postcards' perhaps using cut-out pictures from holiday brochures. Have a shop selling a range of postcards. Make it an informal drama. Let the children write postcards home, deliver them to numbered 'houses' and read the cards aloud to neighbours.

Noisy Traffic

Materials Rough paper, pencils, felt tips.

Discussion Listen to the traffic noises from the window or at the school gate. Can you tell from the sound what kind of vehicle is on its way? Encourage children to find words to express each different sound. Read 'Noisy Traffic'. Look for the pattern of the poem and make up more verses.

Use Work in pairs or groups to make up the longest possible poem, following the 'Noisy Traffic' pattern.

Extension Read the poem out as a choral piece. Make up more poems using the same pattern. It would work well for noisy animals at the zoo. Your new poem might begin like this:

> Day and night, day and night
> The angry lion went
> roar! roar!
> In the zoo, in the zoo.

What can you do with a . . . ?

Materials Rough paper, pencils, felt tips, a selection of everyday objects.

Discussion Look carefully at an ordinary pencil with the children. Ask what it is for, apart from writing with! (It could be a flag pole for a sand castle; an arrow for a small Red Indian; a clothes prop for a garden gnome: the more fantastic the better.) Read Judith Nicholls' poem. Now look at the scissors, fork and saucepan etc and gather more ideas.

Use Get the children to write out a list of ideas for a range of ordinary objects. Put them together to make a poem called 'What can you do with a . . .?'

Extension Make a long zigzag book showing extraordinary uses for ordinary objects. Use it for display. Call the book 'Inventions' and let the children dress up as eccentric inventors!

Animal Parade

Materials Rough paper, pencils.

Discussion Spend a moment or two counting in tens. Listen to the initial sounds. Read the poem 'Animal parade' emphasising the beginning of each word.

Use Let the children work in groups or pairs. Let them work on rough paper to find alliterative animal names, then what they might do, again keeping the beginning sounds the same. Let the groups compete against each other to find the most amusing lines which match the original pattern. Read the finished poems aloud together.

Extension Make up another poem using numbers up to ten. They need not necessarily be about animals. One of the poems might start off like this:

> One washing machine washing the clothes
> Two toasters toasting our tea
> Three . . .

Puppet Talk

Materials Rough paper, pencils, felt tips, paper bags, elastic bands.

Discussion Tell the children the beginning of a story. Let them know that they are going to be allowed to finish it as they like.

Once upon a time there were two giants. One was called Lazybones, the other Noisylungs. They lived on either side of the tallest mountain in the land. Every morning they began by shouting insults at one another.

One morning, just as the sun was beginning to climb into the sky, Noisylungs shouted in a voice that could be heard right across the land, 'Good morning, Lazybones. I don't suppose *you* are up yet!'

Lazybones took a deep breath and shouted back, 'Good morning, Noisylungs. *I've* been up for hours. I bet you haven't started yet. Too busy shouting at me!'

But Noisylungs boasted, 'I've fed the cat and washed the dishes *and* I've watered the garden. Beat that if you can!'

Take suggestions as to how the story might continue, concentrating on the speech itself.

Use Let the children work in pairs. Make simple paper bag puppets attached to the children's hands by elastic bands. Let the pairs choose each to be one of the giants. Suggest the way in which the conversation might go on. Write down what each giant says using blue for one, red for the other. Arrange the conversation in lines like a poem.

Extension Act out the conversation or argument poem using paper bag puppets.

Coloured Flags

Materials Rough paper, pencils, string or wool, staples, scissors, wax or pencil crayons.

Discussion Talk about things that are always (or usually) of one colour. Show children a pot of buttercups, celandines or dandelions or some blades of grass, cress, lettuce etc. Talk about what blue, red or yellow means to them. Talk about favourite colours, the colour of different moods. Note down a few ideas.

Use Using rough paper let the children make a simple list of things around them that are usually yellow, green or blue. Let them choose the ideas they like best, then make sentences beginning 'Yellow is . . .', Blue is . . .' etc. Use one colour only on each sheet. Transfer the idea to the cut-out flag shape. Make more flags, a separate one for each colour. Put the colour poem on one flag and colour over lightly using wax or pencil crayon.

String the poetry flags together across the classroom.

Extension Make a tall poetry tree with colour poems on leaf or flower shapes.

Make a graph of favourite colours.

Our Garden Shed

Materials Rough paper, pencils, felt tips or coloured pencils.

Discussion Talk about garden sheds, garages, attics, storage places where the door is not often opened, where old forgotten things are left to gather dust.

Use A list is a good way to begin a poem. Make a list of the things that might be found inside a garden shed where the door is not often opened. Encourage the children to listen to the beat of the words as they say them over. If the rhythm is right, a poem will grow out of the list. Transfer the list poem to the open door space. Think of a title for the poem.

Extension Make further list poems: things found in the attic, the kitchen, inside a suitcase packed for holidays, inside the sack that Father Christmas carries; a list poem of animals in the zoo, of animals in the farmyard, animals of the jungle. Write the poems into a door space (attic, kitchen, zoo, farmyard), inside a suitcase or sack, between two tall trees for the jungle poem.

Mini-beast Poems

Materials Rough paper, pencils, pencil crayons.

Discussion Talk about the shape a snake, worm or caterpillar makes. Draw the shape in the air. Talk about words to describe snakes, worms and caterpillars. Read the poem 'Snake' by Ernest Rogers. Draw the children's attention to the pattern the words make.

Use Make word lists to describe what a worm looks like, the way it moves etc. Cut the words down, so that the children can write them out with one or two words only on a line. Write out the worm poem following the snake shape.

Extension Use the same method to write snail, caterpillar, or cobweb poems.

House Poem

Materials Rough paper, pencils, felt tips.

Discussion Look at pictures of houses. Talk about what the children's own houses look like. What does every house have? Roof, walls, door, windows. Talk about the shape, colour, use of each. What do they look like? Introduce the chart.

Use Use the answers in the chart as the basis of each mini-poem. Make good use of any unusual features. Try them out on rough paper. Get the children to draw their own house and write the mini-poems into the appropriate space. They might like to follow the shape.

Extension Draw a tree and write a mini-poem for each part of the tree; branches, roots, trunk, tree-top.

The Magic Key

Materials Rough paper, pencils, felt tips or pencil crayons, scissors, blank A4 paper for the finished poem, staples.

Discussion Talk about fairy stories where children have found themselves in magic lands e.g. *Alice in Wonderland*. Read of the discovery in *The Secret Garden*. Suggest that the children might make up a story poem about what they find behind a magic door. Read the opening paragraphs of the sheet as the beginning of a story which the children might finish in their own way. Talk over ideas.

Use Write out an ideas list on rough paper. Make it into a story poem. Listen for the rhythm. Cut out the door shape on the sheet and fold back the doors. Staple a blank sheet of A4 inside and write out the finished poem so that it is visible when the doors are folded back. Colour the picture.

Extension Make a 'street' of magic doors, each folded back to reveal the story poems.

Write a story poem of a cave, going back in time; or a pirate ship, seen through the open hold.

The Fantastic Forest

Materials Rough paper, pencils, felt tips or pencil crayons.

Discussion Talk about how advertis-ments are worded, what they are trying to do. What special words apply to the world of advertising? Look at adverts in the newspaper, talk about adverts on TV. Talk about different kinds of boots and shoes. Make a word list.

Use Colour the Shoe Tree and add other boots and shoes to it. Using the word list make up an advert which will make other people want to visit the Shoe Tree. Make the advert very short. Fill in the space on the sheet. Encourage children to imagine other trees which might grow in the Fantastic Forest. Make up a rhyming jingle for TV or radio.

Extension Make up rhyming adverts/songs for an 'away-day' visit to Ginger-bread Towers, the People Zoo, an Underground Fairground, the Pearly Queen's Palace.

Asking Questions

Materials Rough paper, pencils, felt tips or coloured pencils, scissors.

Discussion Use an encyclopaedia. Look at the questions it poses. Invite the children to suggest things they would like an answer to. Read 'Asking questions'. Encourage unusual/surreal questions e.g. 'What shape is a thingumajig?', 'Can a caterpillar sneeze?'

Use The children might work in pairs or groups for this task. Make a suggestion list and choose the most effective questions. If this poem rhymes, so much the better.

Extension Have a class quiz with wacky questions and answers.

Colour the Sun

Write your ideas about a hot sunny day as rays from the sun. You could rule pencil lines first to help.

The clouds are like cotton wool

I play outside

Now you could write a moon poem, about things that happen at night.

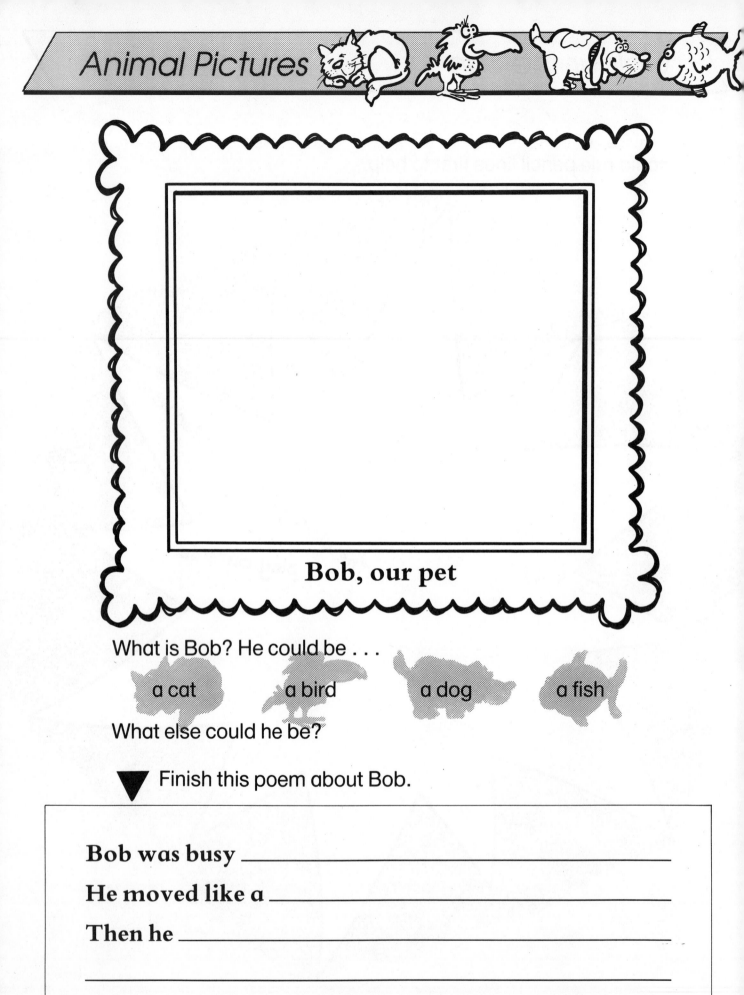

Bob, our pet

What is Bob? He could be . . .

a cat   a bird   a dog   a fish

What else could he be?

▼ Finish this poem about Bob.

Bob was busy _____

He moved like a _____

Then he _____

_____

What noises does Bob make? Put the sound in the last line.

New Nursery Rhymes

Jenny had a little cat

Its coat W_ _ grey a_ smoke

It followed her a_ _ _ _ _ _ t_ _

h_ _ _ _

And very nearly S_ _ _ _ _

Now you try!

Terry had a tiny mouse

_____

_____

_____

Sally had a hungry hen

_____

_____

_____

Balloons and Kites

Balloon

as
big as ball
as round as sun . .
I tug and pull you
when you run and
when wind blows
I say pol-
itely

HOLD ME TIGHTLY

Colleen Thibaudeau

Try to find
'kite' words
to fill the
kite.

as
high as
clouds...

Now you could try
a hot air balloon.

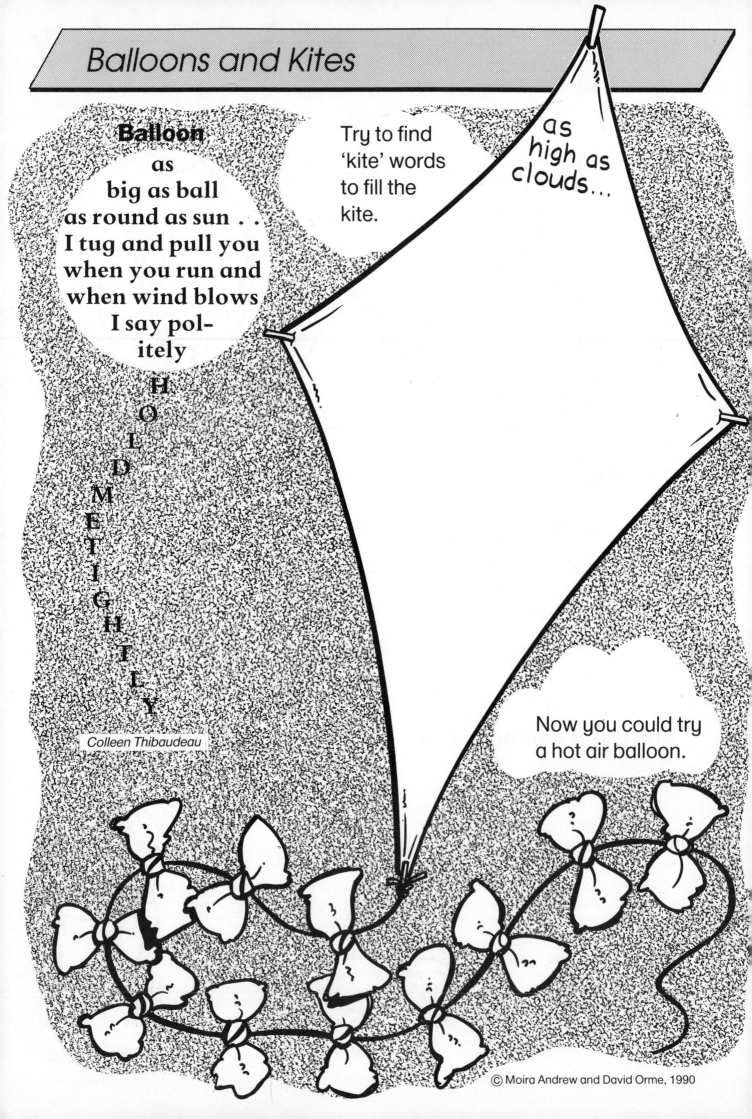

Spider Plant

A Spider plant can be . . .

a volcano firing red hot lava in the air

a deadly deep sea octopus

a boy who hates to have his hair cut

or a weeping willow tree.

Cut out and complete the jigsaw
puzzle. You will be able
to read the poem.

the corn

from the

ue piece

or

at

The gre

hedge

Th har

op si w

saw is do

n the mid

ater the

rt

ky

ure

re

ers

e edge

is s

ne.

ne.

dle

un

dle

zl

en es

der the p

jigs

The jigs

Now fill i

The gre

ne

Find all

Then bits

Th

bl

The Magic Box

I will put in the box

A little kitten playing about
A pair of sparkling shoes
And some diamonds

I will put in the box
A river with wishes
A Father Christmas
A movie of The Snowman

I will put in the box
The first Christmas and
    the last snowman
The sound of children playing
And the birds singing

Chloe Whitt Age 7

Chloe has put in her magic box some of the things she likes best.

Here is a magic box for you to write in.

Five Fat Frogs

Read the counting rhyme and fill in the gaps to make it rhyme.

Five fat frogs
sitting in a row
one got hiccups, hic!
watch him go.

_ _ _ _ fat frogs
peeping round a frond
one got the jitters
and _ _ _ _ _ _ _ _ _ _ _ _ _ _ _

_ _ _ _ _ fat frogs
on a lily pad
one waddled off
because he was _ _ _

_ _ _ fat frogs
lying in the sun
one got sunburned
then _ _ _ _ _ _ _ _ _ _ _

_ _ _ fat frog
sitting on a stone
he began to cry
because he _ _ _ _ _ _ _

No fat frogs
going out to play
perhaps they'll come back
the next _ _ _ _ _ _ _ _

Five Black Cats

5 _____

_____

_____

_____

4 _____

_____

_____

_____

3 _____

_____

_____

_____

2 _____

_____

_____

_____

1 _____

_____

_____

_____

Trog

"Flints for eyes, old stone head,
That's me
Way down beneath you,
With bones for company.
I've granite teeth too
For gnawing the dead,
I hear you laughing
Over my head –
Just wait till they put you
Down here"
He said.

David Orme

Now you be a monster!
In your poem say:
► What your name is
  (that could be your title)
► What you look like
► What you are made of
► What you do
► What you might do!

What's in the Pudding?

What's in the pudding?

What's in the pud?
What's in the pud?
Stir it round
To make it good!

A pound of currants
A bag of flour
Some Chinese spare ribs
Sweet and sour,
Tomatoes, a dollop
of Stilton cheese,
A pinch of pepper
(Watch out, don't sneeze)
Some sugar that's brown,
Some sugar that's white,
Some peas, some sticks
Of dynamite,
Roll in a cloth,
Soak it in beer,
Bake in the oven
Until next year!

David Orme

Now it's your turn

What's in the Stew?

What's in the stew?
What's in the stew?
This is what
You have to do!

_____

_____

_____

_____

_____

_____

_____

_____

_____

_____

Poetry Clock

"Put your chairs on the tables"
I'm in such a hurry
Mine falls off with a crash
And I have to stay behind!

3

Dad's turn to make the tea.
"Sausages and beans today"
Its always sausage and beans
When Dad makes the tea.

4

"I've had a terrible day"
Says my sister. "Awful"
Maybe once she'll have a
good day.
It hasn't happened yet.

5

"Stop making that row!
We can't hear the news"
Why do they bother?
The news only makes them
grumpy.

6

Now write your clock poem on the lines and put the hour in the box.
Cut round the clock, and cut out the black strips. Slot the poem through these.

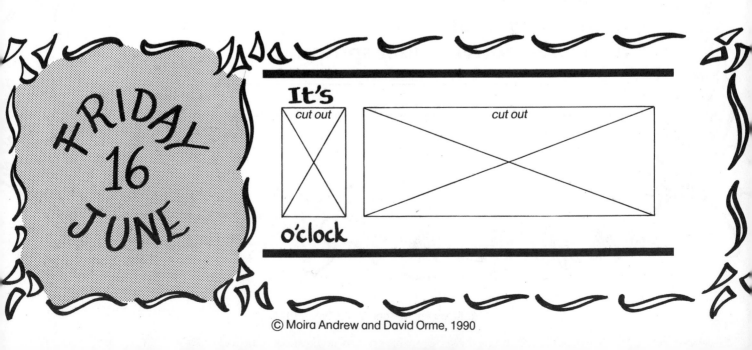

FRIDAY 16 JUNE

It's

cut out

cut out

o'clock

What's in the Box?

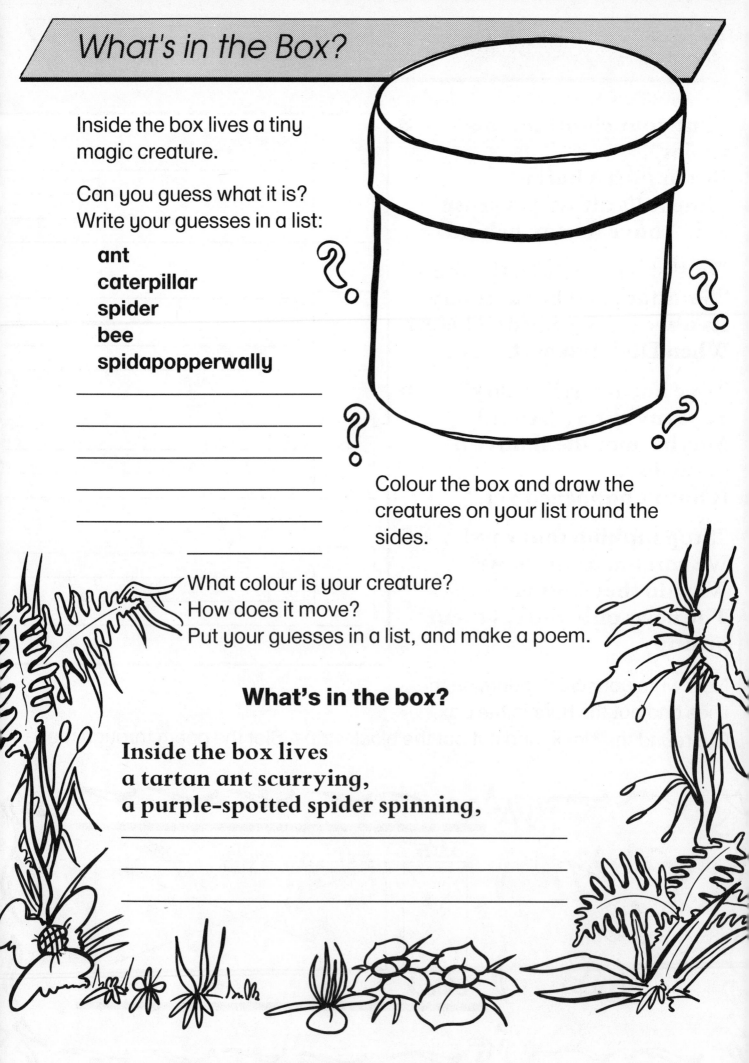

Inside the box lives a tiny
magic creature.

Can you guess what it is?
Write your guesses in a list:

ant
caterpillar
spider
bee
spidapopperwally

_____

_____

_____

_____

_____

Colour the box and draw the
creatures on your list round the
sides.

What colour is your creature?
How does it move?
Put your guesses in a list, and make a poem.

What's in the box?

**Inside the box lives
a tartan ant scurrying,
a purple-spotted spider spinning,**

_____

_____

Weather Words

Go outside on a rainy day and listen to the rain.
Make a list of rain words.

Say them in your head until they sound right, and write them in a rain
pattern on the umbrella.

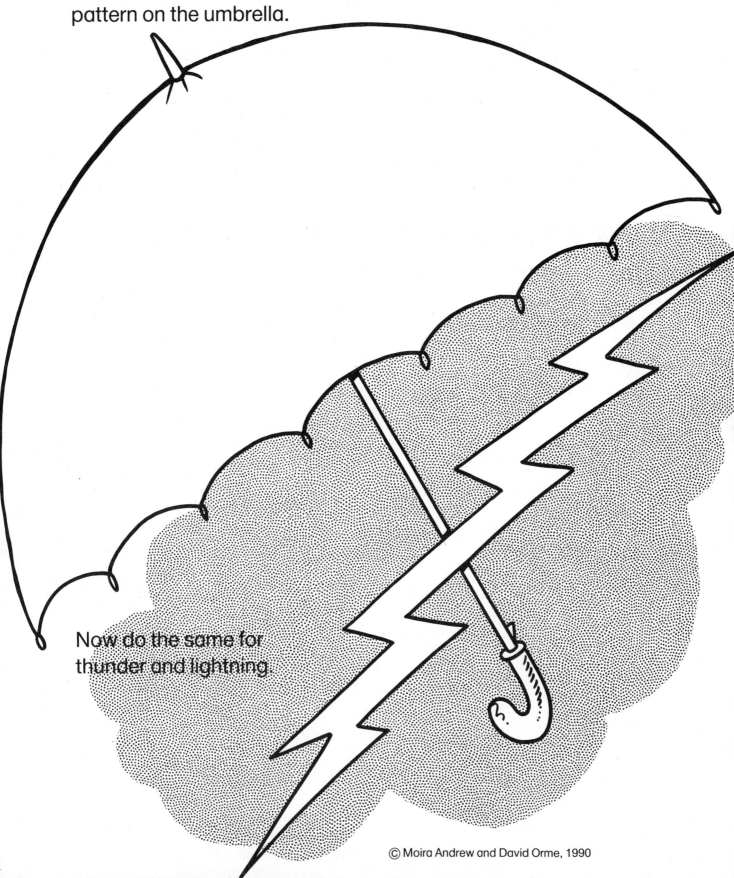

Now do the same for
thunder and lightning

Flying Poems

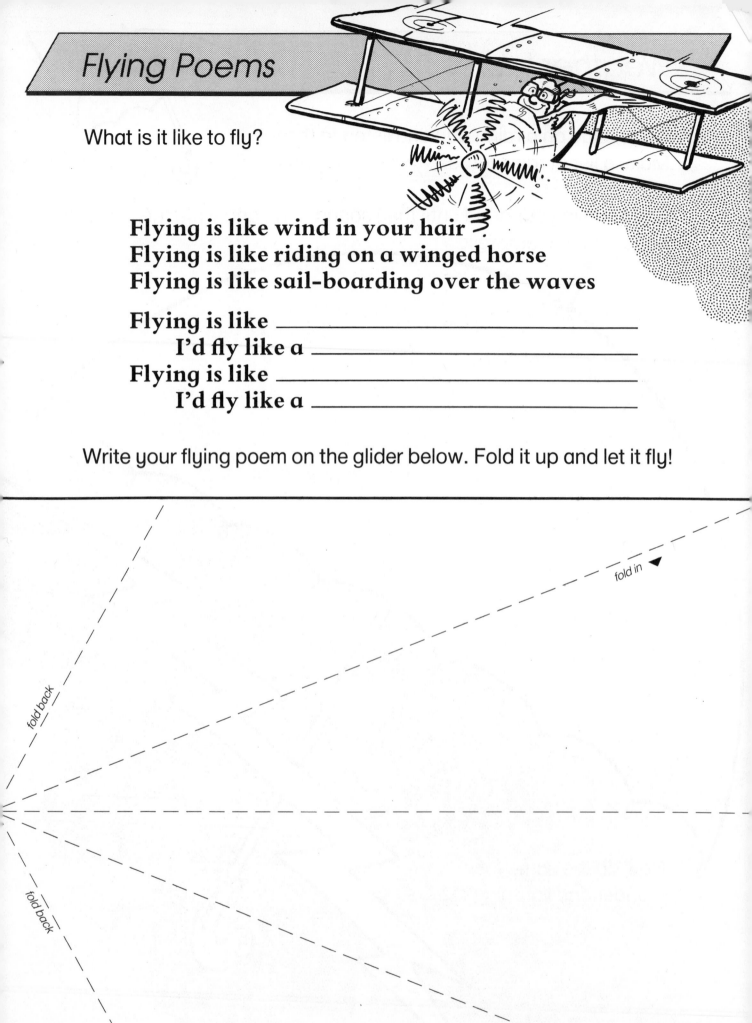

What is it like to fly?

Flying is like wind in your hair
Flying is like riding on a winged horse
Flying is like sail-boarding over the waves

Flying is like _____
  I'd fly like a _____
Flying is like _____
  I'd fly like a _____

Write your flying poem on the glider below. Fold it up and let it fly!

fold in ▶

fold back

fold back

fold in ▶

Summer is ...

Think about what makes summer special for you.

Is it going off to the beach and paddling in the sea?
Is it the sound of bees, the song of crickets in the grass?
Is it the sight of tall yellow sunflowers growing in the garden?

Make a collection of your own ideas about summer, using just a few words, enough to make a picture in your mind.

Summer is the buzzing of bees.

Summer is

The Quietest Thing in the World

worm

What is the quietest little creature you can think of? Put your pictures in the spaces.

What silent things might they do? They can be quite magic if you like. Imagine a beetle dancing in golden shoes or a ladybird writing a long letter to her friend across the seas.

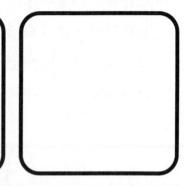

Make a list of small creatures and the magic things they can do. Draw them in the boxes. A poem will grow as you go along.

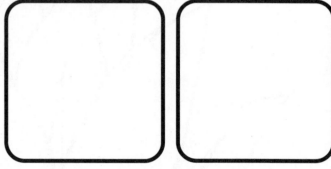

The Quietest Things in the World

The first lick of the lolly

The first lick of the lolly
The first bite of the cake,
There is something about them
You cannot mistake.

The first day of the holidays,
The first time you wear
Something new, then that feeling
So special is there.

Think of all the 'first best' things which make life exciting. List them and say them in your head. Then write your poem.

The first time you open
A new comic the smell
Of the ink and the paper
Is exciting as well.

The very first bike ride,
The first dip in the sea,
The first time on a boat
Were all thrilling to me.

The first page of a book,
The first words of a play
The first thing at morning
When you start a new day

John Cotton

Chorus Poems

A chorus poem has the same words at the end of each verse.

Darren Edwards thumps the drums; he's the loudest in the town.

Abigail Thompson made new shakers, filled yogurt pots with shiny beans.

Bang, bang, shake and rattle Listen to the band.

Bang, bang, shake and rattle. Listen to the band.

Finish the poem by using the names of people in your class and the instruments they like to play.

Always finish with a chorus.

Write the chorus under the TV. Cut out the TV screen and black slots. Write your chorus poem on the strip and slot it through the slits. Now you can read your poem on TV.

cut line

cut line

Darren Edwards
thumps the drums;
he's the loudest
in the town.

slot poem through here ▶

cut out

Bang, bang, shake and rattle. Listen to the band.

Days of the Week

days	what happens	how you feel	colour
Monday	• back to school	• sad	• blue
Tuesday	•	•	•
Wednesday	•	•	•
Thursday	•	•	•
Friday	•	•	•
Saturday	•	•	•
Sunday	•	•	•

First fill in the chart.

Now put everything together, starting every second line with a new day.

Monday is back-to-school day
It's a sad and blue day
Tuesday is singing-songs-in-the-hall day
_____

Try putting your own poem in the calendar below.

colour

Monday	_____	
Tuesday	_____	
Wednesday	_____	
Thursday	_____	
Friday	_____	
Saturday	_____	
Sunday	_____	

Sad Face, Happy Face

Talk about what has made each face look like this. Write the words on the faces, some sad, some happy.

Now make a mask big enough to cover your face. Work with a friend. One make a happy face, one make a sad one.

cross

smiling

Make up a conversation with bright, happy words from the happy face and sad, bleak words from the other. Then make up a conversation poem from your words.

Magic Spell

What horrid, disgusting things will you put in the pot?
Add them to this spell.

Eye of snake
Tail of rat
Two half coconuts
And a very fat

Pink worm
Skin off the custard
Six stinging nettles
And Dad's mustard

Coloured sock
With a hole in the toe
Three cowpats
And oh!

I've forgotten . . .

_____

_____

_____

Expanding Poems

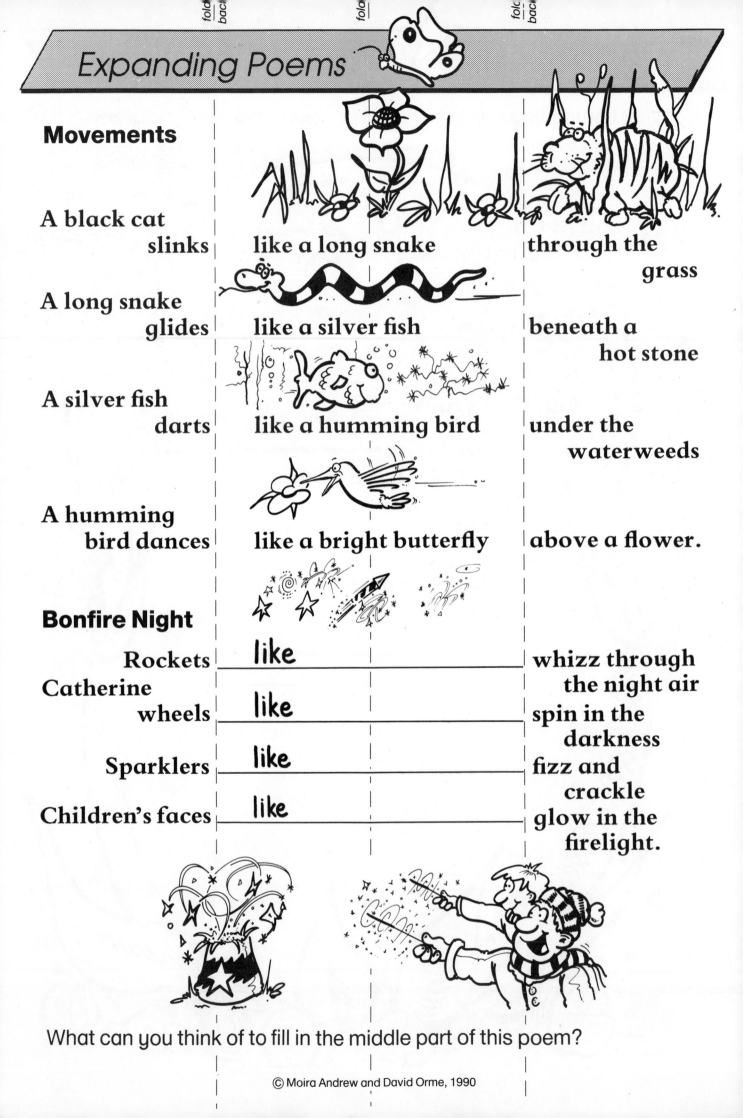

Movements

A black cat
    slinks   like a long snake   through the
                                               grass

A long snake
    glides   like a silver fish   beneath a
                                               hot stone

A silver fish
    darts   like a humming bird   under the
                                               waterweeds

A humming
    bird dances   like a bright butterfly   above a flower.

Bonfire Night

Rockets   like _____   whizz through
                                               the night air

Catherine
    wheels   like _____   spin in the
                                               darkness

Sparklers   like _____   fizz and
                                               crackle

Children's faces   like _____   glow in the
                                               firelight.

What can you think of to fill in the middle part of this poem?

Good Things to Eat

What do you like the best to eat?

Make a list of your favourite foods.

Can you describe them in a special way? Add them to the menu.

Try out these ideas with other foods. Write your poem on the plate below.

MENU

Six sizzling sausages
Meaty half-pounder hamburgers
Yummy chocolate ice-cream with raspberry sauce dripping like beads of b.l.o.o.d. YUK!

Good Things to Eat

I like Soft-boiled Eggs

I like soft-boiled eggs.
I like liver.
I like chicken legs
And jelly. See it
       shiver.
I like cabbage –
All kinds of greens.
I like sausages
And bubbling brown
       baked beans.

John Kitching

Wind Streamers

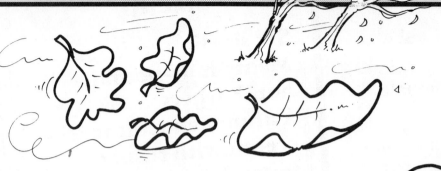

What sounds does the wind make?
Make up a song of the wind.

Trees whisper
Leaves sigh
Branches _____
Seeds _____
Dustbin lids _____
Wires _____

_____

_____

Try to think of unusual words.

Collect your ideas for a windy day poem.

Write one line on each strip of paper.
Cut them out and pin
them to a stick.
Then make your poem
fly by running with your
streamer stick in the wind.

© Moira Andrew and David Orme, 1990

Angry Child, Happy Child

When I'm angry, I feel _____

Make a list of angry words:

cross
furious
mad as a lion

_____
_____
_____
_____
_____

Put a picture of your angry face in the space. Write some angry words in the speech balloon.

Grrrr!

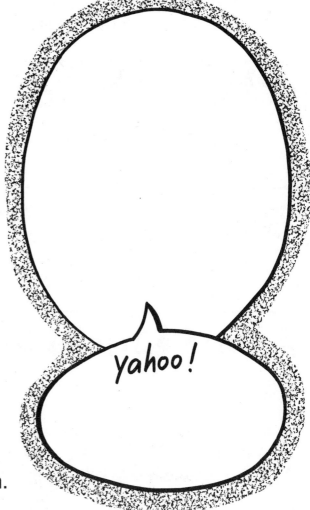

yahoo!

When I'm happy I feel _____

Make a list of happy words:

smiling
sunny
cheerful as a chicken

_____
_____
_____
_____
_____

Put a picture of your happy face in this space. Write some happy words in the speech balloon.

Now make a conversation poem. Use the angry and happy words you have written.

Christmas Chains

Think about what Christmas means to *you*. Make a list:

parties
Baby Jesus
snow
dressing up

_____
_____
_____
_____
_____
_____
_____

Now put your ideas into a sentence.
Begin each one, 'Christmas is . . .'

Christmas is the sound of church bells.

Christmas is lights on the tree.

Christmas is . . .

Now write one line on each strip of paper, and colour them in different colours.
Cut them out and make a Christmas poetry chain.

glue or paste

Christmas is

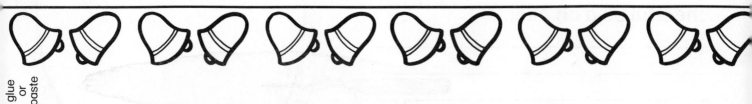

glue or paste

glue or paste

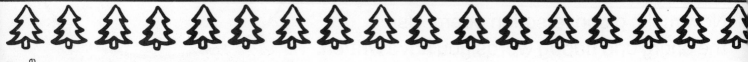

glue or paste

Paper Boat

2 fold back ▼

5 fold in double sheet ▼

4 fold in double sheet ▼

_____

_____

_____

_____

_____

_____

(write your message poem here)

Before you make your boat, think about where it might sail to and what adventures it could have. What will the weather be like?

1 fold in ▼

Give your boat a storybook name in the box below and write your message poem in the space above.

Paper Boat

**Make a little paper boat
Take it to the river,
If it swims and stays afloat
You will live forever.**

Gerda Mayer

3 fold back ▼

Colour the postcards
using bright colours.
Make up a short poem
about one picture.
Write it on the back of the
postcard.

Summer Picture

A blue boat
dances
across glass-green waves
its white sails
fluttering
like butterflies

Moira Andrew

Noisy Traffic

Day and night, day and night,
The bicycle bell went   ring! ring!

Up the hill, up the hill.
Day and night, day and night,
The bicycle bell went   ring! ring!

The motor bike went   buzz! buzz!

Up the hill, up the hill
Day and night, day and night,
The bicycle bell went   ring! ring!

The motor bike went   buzz! buzz!

The little car went   honk! honk!

Up the hill, up the hill.

Look at the pictures of traffic going up the hill. What noises do they make?
Put the noises in the boxes underneath. Use the noises to add to the poem.
What other traffic could be going up the hill?

What can you  do with a ...?

What can you do with a pencil?

You can sharpen it
or break the point,
trap it in the door;
fasten it behind your ear
or tap it on the floor;
use it as a walking stick
(if you're very small).
Dig a hole to plant a seed,
tap it on a wall;
use it as a handy splint
for rabbits' broken legs;
stir your coffee
stir your tea –
stir up all the dregs!

Drop it from a table top,
pop it in a case;
use it as a lollystick,
send it up in space!
Two will give you chopsticks,
one could pick a lock;
bore a hole and thread one
to darn a hole-y sock . . .

These are just a few ideas,
there must be hundreds more –
but meantime, trap it, snap it,
flap it,

TAP IT ON THE FLOOR!

Judith Nicholls

Choose one of these objects, or one of your own, for your own poem called

What can you do with a...?

_____

_____

_____

_____

_____

_____

_____

_____

Animal Parade

The animals are on parade today, and we need your help to finish the poem.

Ten tortoises touching their toes,

Twenty tigers twitching their tails,

Thirty thrushes, thoughtful and thin,

Forty flamingoes fishing for frogs,

Fifty foxes flying some flags,

Sixty sealions _____

Seventy _____

Eighty earwigs _____

Ninety _____

A hundred _____

Work on the poem in groups. Listen carefully to the sound of the number and make your line match if you can.

Read your finished poems aloud together.

Puppet Talk

First make paper bag puppet giants' heads.

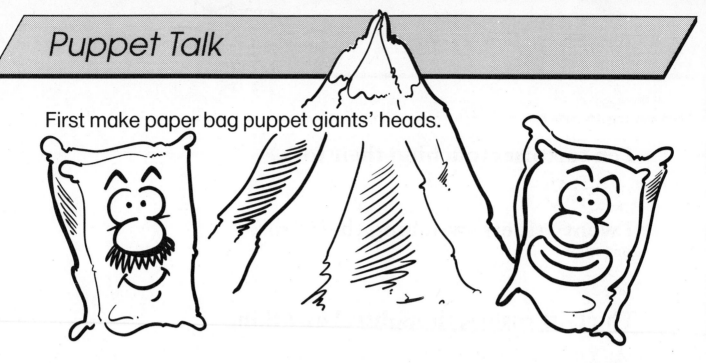

Now work with a partner and have a giant argument. This one is between two giants. Carry on the story, writing Lazybones' words in red, and Noisylungs' in blue. Use the puppets to help you. These giants live on either side of a big mountain, and begin each day by shouting at each other.

NOISYLUNGS: Wake up, Lazybones! Are you still lying in bed?

LAZYBONES: What a racket! You woke me with your shouting!

NOISYLUNGS: I've fed the cat and washed the dishes already! Get up, you lazy old giant!

LAZYBONES: _____

NOISYLUNGS: _____

LAZYBONES: _____

NOISYLUNGS: _____

LAZYBONES: _____
_____

NOISYLUNGS: _____
_____

TOGETHER: _____

Pick a colour, then think of 4 or 5 things that are always that colour.
Maybe you pick yellow. You write, 'Yellow is buttercups'.
Take your idea one step further. 'Yellow is buttercups spilled
like bright paint
across the field.'

Use one colour
for each flag
and fill them
up with your
ideas.

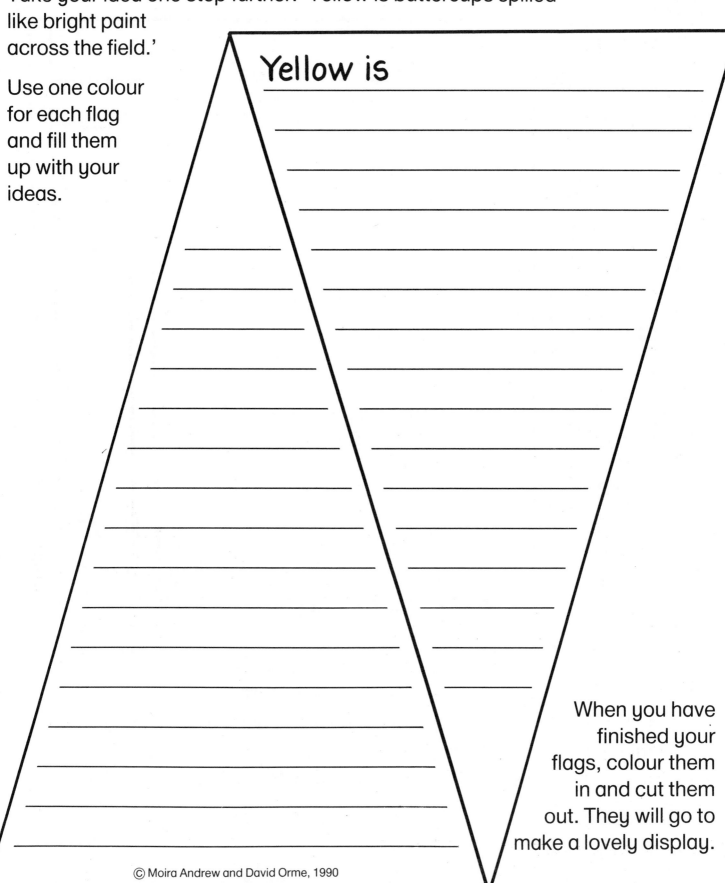

Yellow is

When you have
finished your
flags, colour them
in and cut them
out. They will go to
make a lovely display.

Our Garden Shed

Think of the shed at the bottom of your garden. What's inside?
Cobwebs, rusty garden tools, forgotten pushchairs, broken TV sets?

In the picture is a shed with an open door. Write a list of things you
might find inside. Soon you will see a poem growing. Say the list
over in your head until it sounds right. Listen to the beat, or rhythm.

When you are happy with your list poem, write it neatly into the
door space.

Mini-Beast Poems

The snake
twists
and
bends
as it
sends
itself
along
slithering
slides
and graceful
glides
hissing
and
kissing the
air with its
flickering
tongue.

Snake

Ernest Rogers

Read the poem about a snake.
Use your worm words
to make a poem
about a worm.

Worm

Now you can make a
snail poem.
Use the shape of a
snail shell.
Or you could try a
spider's web poem.

House Poem

	shape	colour	made of	what for?	looks like
roof	tent	green	tiles	keep out weather	mountain
door					
walls					
windows					

Use the chart to start making a house poem.

roof: **Green, shaped like a tent**
Made of tiles
To keep out the wind
and the rain
Looks like a mountain top.

walls:

door:

windows:

Draw your house. Write each poem in the right place.

The roof is a mountain top
layered with green tiles
like a bird's feathers
to keep us warm

The roof is like a
green tent, made of tiles.
Sharp as a mountain top
it keeps out wind and rain.

The Magic Key

You are alone on a sunny day. You find a shining key in the long grass.
You pick it up, turning it over and over in your hands.
Then you notice a wooden doorway in the wall beside you. The key fits!
Very slowly you push one door open.
Tell what you see on the other side of the magic doorway. Make your
adventures into a story poem.
Cut along the solid lines in the picture so that the magic doors will open,
and paste your poem inside.

The Fantastic Forest

Imagine visiting a fantastic forest where trees grow boots and shoes. On the Amazing Shoe Tree there are trainers, high-heels, slippers, Doc Marten boots and lots more.

Colour the picture and add other boots and shoes to the branches. Think how you might get other people to visit the Shoe Tree. Look in the newspapers for words that appear in advertisements.

AMAZING SUPER

Excellent Value

Unique Opportunity

Make up your own advert in the space below:

VISIT THE AMAZING SHOE TREE

What other unusual trees grow in the fantastic forest? Pyjama Trees, Sweet Trees, School Dinner Trees?

Draw your own tree picture and make up an advertising jingle for TV.

Asking Questions

Asking Questions

Who first thought of shoeing horses?
How did they know it wouldn't hurt?
When was the toilet roll invented?
How much ink can a squid squirt?
Whose idea was the tooth fairy?
What shape is a thingumajig?
How can each snowflake be different?
Did primeval man play tig?
Why does frost make leafy patterns?
Can a caterpillar sneeze?
Why do Eskimos rub noses?
Help me find the answers, please.

Sue Cowling

Do you know the answers to any of these questions?
Make up answers to as many as you can.
Now think of some surprising questions of your own. Make a Questions Poem.
Write it in the box. Which is your most curious question? Write that one
in the small box to go in a class display.

cut line

?????????????????????????????

_____
_____
_____
_____
_____
_____
_____
_____
_____
_____
_____
_____

?????????????????????????????